SUPER SMART

Memory Puzzles

ARCTURUS

CONTENTS

TIPS ON MEMORY PUZZLES FROM ELSIE

Here are some helpful hints from Elsie.
Remember, elephants never forget!

Look carefully at the first picture in each puzzle to fix it in your mind.

Turn the page and find out what you have to do. If you get REALLY stuck, flick back to the first picture.

Keep an image in your mind of where items appear on the page.

Look for patterns in the pictures that will help you to remember the important parts.

HOW THIS BOOK WORKS

Each puzzle works across two pages. Start on the righthand page and read the instructions, then turn over and find out how well you have remembered things. There are no answer pages, as you can turn back to check your results. Try to remember as much as you can before you turn back to see how well you have done.

BUSY BEES

This scene is buzzing with activity! Take a close look, and then turn over.

BUSY BEES

How many additional bees have arrived in the time it took to turn the page? Circle them as you find them to help you keep track.

Super ceramics

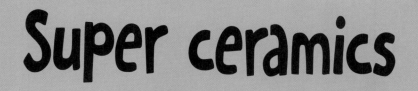

Tilly, Milly, and Lily have painted their own designs onto ceramics. Study their works of art, and then turn the page.

Super ceramics

Can you remember what the three girls painted? Recreate their designs here.

8

ZOO CREW

ZOO

Do you love the zoo? Have a look round this one, and try to remember everything you see.

ZOO CREW

ZOO

Can you draw the animals that should be in each empty enclosure?

SCHOOL TRIP

Sandwiches
Drink
Camera
Pens
Waterproof coat
Spare socks
Sunglasses
Sunblock
Hat
Apple

Hazy Maisie has a terrible memory! Her dad has written her a list of all the things she needs to pack. Try to remember the list, and then turn the page to help.

SCHOOL TRIP

Can you find each of the items that Maisie needs with her tomorrow?

Hint
There were 10 items on Maisie's list.

Look at the cards in this hand, and then turn the page to continue the game.

PLAY THE GAME

The player has picked up a five of spades. Which of these hands of cards is hers?

1

2

3

4

Pablo is daydreaming about last night's buffet. Take a look at all the goodies he could choose from.

A fine feast

A fine feast

Here is today's spread.
Which item is no longer
available, and what has
replaced it?

Par for the course

Take a look at these golfers on the course.
What holes are they playing? Now turn the page...

Par for the course

One of the golfers has got muddled and moved on to the wrong hole. Can you figure out which one?

Mrs. Merryweather the florist has made a pretty bunch of flowers for a wedding.

BLOOMING BRILLIANT

Take a look at the glorious blooms for the bride, and then turn the page.

BLOOMING BRILLIANT

Mark the buckets to show which flowers Mrs. Merryweather used. Put a cross next to the flowers that she didn't need.

LOST PROPERTY

All of these items have been handed in to the office. Take a look at who these items belong to and then turn the page.

LOST PROPERTY

These children have all come to look for their belongings.
Which child's item has not been found?

Teresa

Jack

Payal

Lucy

Hattie

Dan

Warren

Hugo

Nala

Try to remember each of the paint splats as they appear here, and then turn the page to test your memory.

Splat attack

Can you answer these questions?

1 What shape are the red splats?
Are they a, b, or c?

a ✹   b ✷   c ✻

2 What shade do you get if you mix
all four corner splats together?

3 What happens if you mix the
third row with any other paints?

4 How many blue splats
are there?

5 What does the bottom
row look like?

FANCY FISH

Chico wants to buy three fish for his tropical tank at home. There are so many to choose from! Study the tank carefully.

FANCY FISH

Now look at the tank again to see which fish are missing. Which three bags contain fish that were in the tank before?

Child's play

Toby has found his baby toys. He used to love this shape sorter! Take a look at the two sides on show.

Toby needs six pieces, but has found only five. Which piece does he need to look for in the bottom of the toy box?

Stick-a-pic

Josie has been busy in the art room!
Study her collage, and then
turn to the next page.

Stick-a-pic

Look at the stickers along the bottom of the page. Which three do you need to add to make this collage identical to Josie's?

a

b

c

d

e

Glossary

belongings The things that belong to you.

ceramics Objects, such as vases and bowls, made of clay and hardened in a kiln oven.

collage A picture made using scraps of paper, material, and similar things.

enclosure A fenced or walled area to keep in animals.

hand The cards you have to play with in any game of cards.

identical Exactly the same.

Further Information

Books

Brain Games for Clever Kids by Gareth Moore, Buster Books, 2014.

Brain Boosters: Maths Puzzles by Lisa Regan, Arcturus Publishing, 2017.

The Big Book of Kids' Puzzles by Jess Bradley, Arcturus Publishing, 2016.

The Puzzle Activity Book, Buster Books, 2015.

Websites

www.bbc.co.uk/cbbc/games/bp-puzzles-and-riddles-week-15
Have a go at these brainteasers on the BBC website.

www.si.edu/kids
Check out the kids' page from the Smithsonian Museum for fun games and try-at-home activities.

Index

This edition published in 2019 by Arcturus Publishing Limited
26/27 Bickels Yard, 151–153 Bermondsey Street,
London SE1 3HA

Written by Lisa Regan
Illustrated by Steven Wood with Samantha Meredith, Ed Myer, and Graham Rich
Designed by Trudi Webb
Cover designed by Ms Mousepenny

ISBN: 978-1-78950-328-9
CH007000NT
Supplier 33, Date 0119, Print run 8053

Printed in China